Oxford
International
Resources

4

AF148463

Early Years
Activity Book

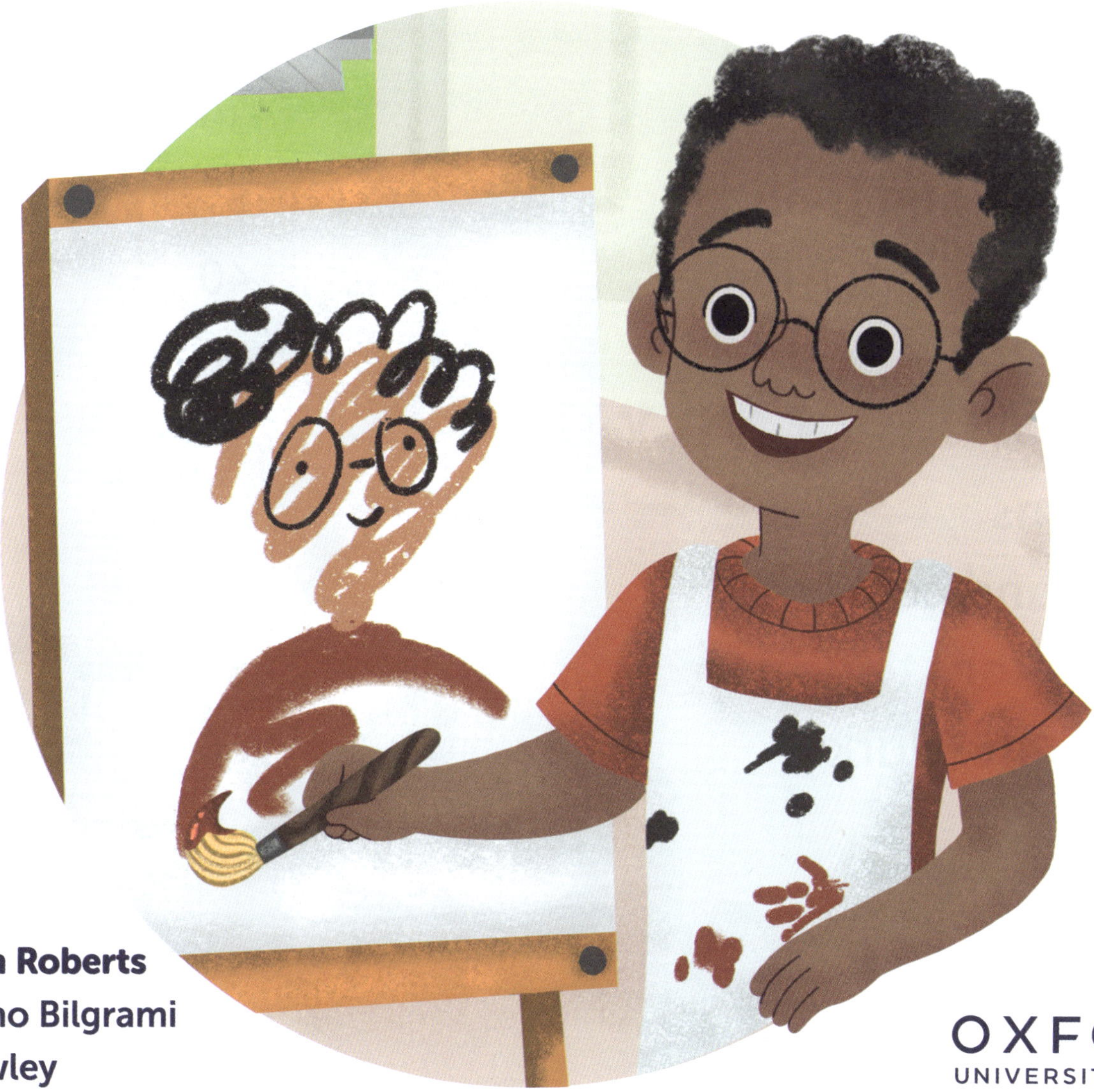

Deborah Roberts
Shahbano Bilgrami
Sue Cowley

OXFORD
UNIVERSITY PRESS

Contents

Happy to be me   3

Watch me grow   4
I can get ready   9
Healthy and tasty   14
From garden to plate   19

Fun with friends   24

Making friends   25
We are friends   30
Being a good friend   35
Exploring with friends   40

The wonderful world   45

Patterns   46
Light and colour   51
From night to day   55
Fun in the dark   60

Happy to be me

In this topic, learners are encouraged to:

- trace and colour, using the correct pencil grip
- count up to 20
- arrange events in the right order
- retell a story
- identify familiar shapes.

Teachers will also help learners to:

- write familiar letters and spell simple words
- explore different ways of showing numbers
- discuss good hygiene, like washing their hands
- explore the world outdoors
- learn about their bodies and how to use them.

Watch me grow

a Sing Happy to be me.

b Look. What are the children doing?

c Find the child being measured.

d Count Gibran's blocks.

At home
Compare a current photo of your child with 1 from the year before. Discuss differences on the outside (e.g. hair, height) and on the inside (e.g. new skills).

In this session, children will also: explore their classroom, try writing their names, decorate hand cut-outs, measure their height, talk about things they can do. → TG pp. 140–143

Watch me grow

Explore

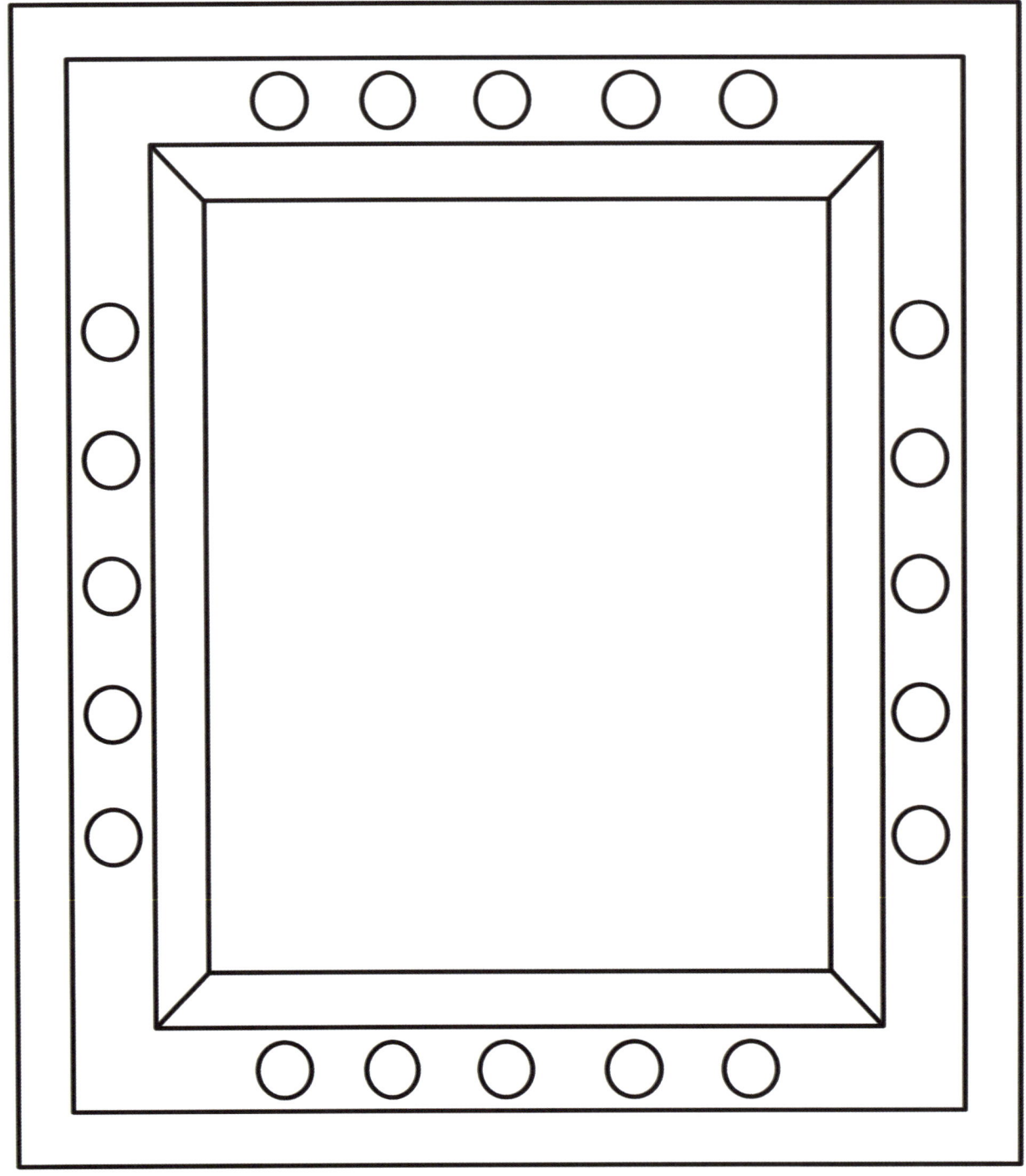

a Draw your face and write your name.

b Colour the circles in a pattern.

At home
Look at some old and new photos of your family and talk to your child about how people (including themselves) have changed. What is different about them then/now?

6 In this session, children will also: practise making patterns, make and use a number track, share stories about being special. → TG pp. 140–143

Watch me grow

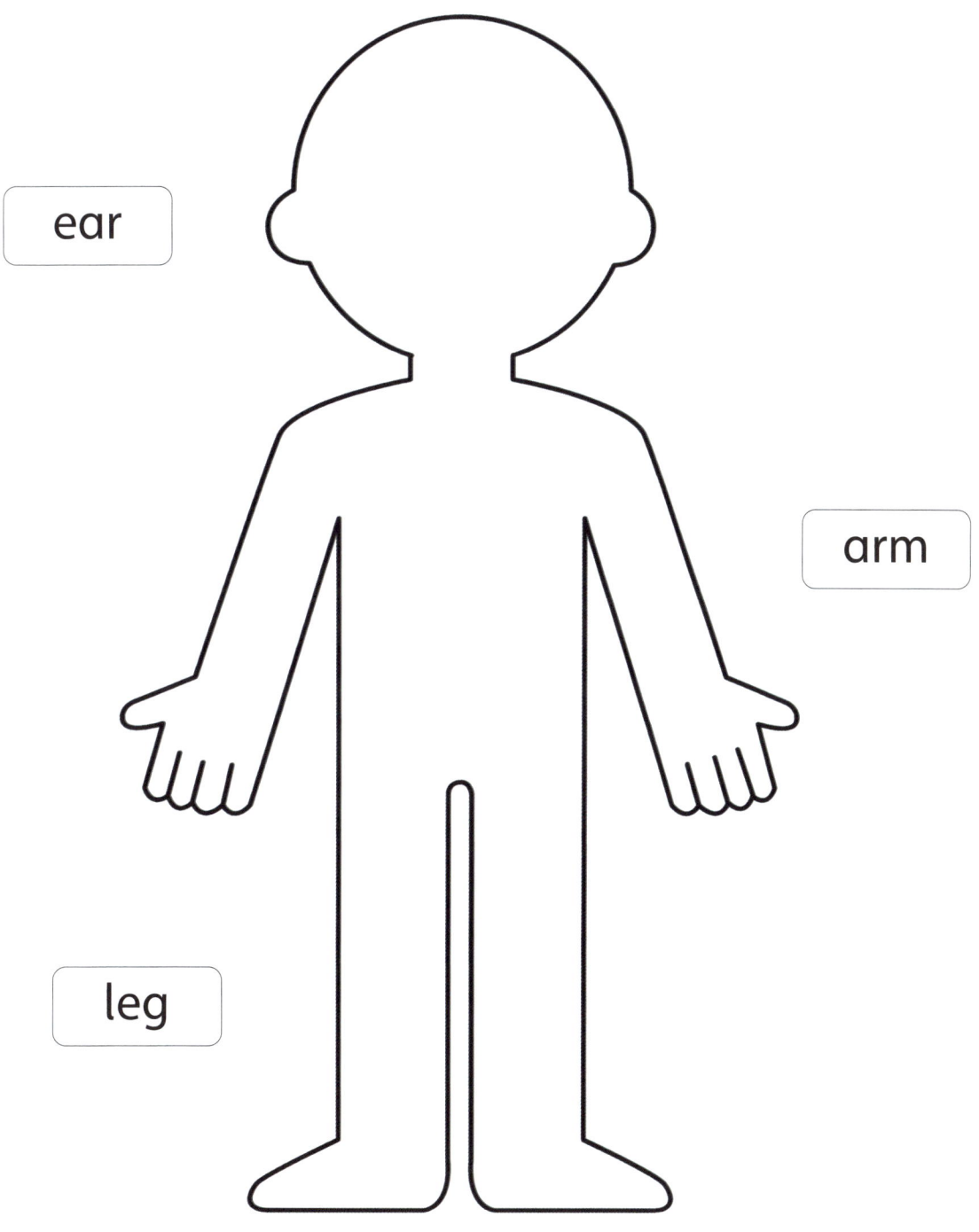

ear

arm

leg

a Draw a face, some hair and clothes.

b Count the number of fingers.

In this session, children will also: practise counting to 20, revise basic shapes, move their bodies in different ways. → TG pp. 140–143

At home

Create collages of people by cutting out different body parts, supporting your child to use scissors or by tearing the pictures out. Name the body parts as you make your creations.

Connect

a Name each shape.

b Match each shape with a picture.

In this session, children will also: make shapes with their bodies, talk about keeping clean, play imaginatively in the home corner. → TG pp. 140–143

At home

Play a game by calling out the names of different parts of the body. How quickly can your child point to them? Then swap roles.

I can get ready

a Mime what the children are doing.

b Count the buttons. Count the zips.

c Find the things we wear in the rain.

At home

Ask your child to practise buttoning and unbuttoning a cardigan while it is on a flat surface in front of them. Ask them to count the buttons.

In this session, children will also: choose outdoor clothes, practise getting changed and using fasteners, hear and count claps. → TG pp. 144–147

Explore

a Listen to your teacher and colour the buttons.

b Tick (✓) the coat with the most buttons.

In this session, children will also: tell a story about going out in cold weather, show number patterns in different ways, practise moving to develop core strength. → TG pp. 144–147

At home

Talk to your child about what they do to get ready for school. Ask: *What do you do first? What do you do next? What do you do last?*

I can get ready

_____

_____

_____

_____

a Write numbers to show the order to get ready for school.

b Say what happens first and last.

In this session, children will also: talk about morning routines, think about what they can do now they are bigger, practise writing, learn about brushing their teeth. → TG pp. 144–147

At home

Support your child to gradually do more of their morning routine by themselves, for example, helping to lay the table for breakfast.

11

I can get ready

a Find the lunch box.

b Look. What has water in it?

c Count the pots with food in them.

In this session, children will also: explore transparent materials, make pictures that light can shine through, practise packing a school bag. → TG pp. 144–147

At home

Find items that are made from materials that you can see through and ones that you cannot. Discuss them with your child and sort them into 2 groups.

I can get ready

a Count the children.

b Colour the sun hats.

c Look. Who has the wrong clothes?

In this session, children will also: prepare for a nature walk, use their senses to notice things on their nature walk, make patterns with natural objects they collect. → TG pp. 144–147

At home
Go outside with your child and look at the place where you live. What can you hear, see, and smell?

Healthy and tasty

a Say the Growing rhyme.

b Find the lettuces.

c Look. What is Maya doing?

d Count the red tomatoes.
Count the watering cans.

At home

Talk about what plants need to stay healthy. If you have indoor or outdoor plants, encourage your child to help look after them.

In this session, children will also: describe vegetables, make pictures of vegetables growing, plant seeds, segment/blend CVC words, help make and taste vegetable snacks. → TG pp. 147–150

15

a Count the number of foods in total.

b Colour the foods you like to eat.

c Look. Which part has the fewest foods?

In this session, children will also: talk about different types of food, sort food on a giant 'eat well' plate, create and play in a pretend food shop. → TG pp. 147–150

At home

Encourage your child to count how many fruits and vegetables they have each day, aiming to have at least 5 portions daily.

Healthy and tasty

a Find a fruit.

b Find and name a vegetable.

c Find the foods that are treats.

In this session, children will also: taste and describe different fruits, compare their likes and dislikes with others, keep count in a throwing game. → TG pp. 147–150

At home

Talk with your child about different foods. Do they prefer certain flavours, like sweet or sour?

Connect

a Look. What are the children doing?

b Colour and count the pieces of fruit in the basket.

In this session, children will also: create and try out their own obstacle course, talk about their feelings, make a collage of a pretend meal. → TG pp. 147–150

At home

Explore outside with your child and talk about stretching, running, jumping, and keeping fit. Talk about the parts of their body that they are using.

From garden to plate

Salad for lunch

a Name the vegetables.

b Retell the story.

In this session, children will also: make a real salad to eat; create pretend food out of modelling dough. → TG pp. 151–153

At home

Make a salad with your child. Ask them to suggest 5 healthy foods you can add to the bowl. Let them be creative!

19

pot

a Trace the dotted lines.
Colour the picture.

b Trace and say the word.

In this session, children will also: decorate plant pots, write a simple phrase on a label, practise counting, walk, run, and hop along different lines outside. → TG pp. 147–150

At home

Choose simple 3-letter words (like 'pot' or 'cat') and ask your child to think of 2 rhyming words for each.

From garden to plate

a **Add the missing numbers.**

b **Tick (✓) the lettuce.**

In this session, children will also: recall a caterpillar's life-cycle, create a caterpillar number track outside, make model caterpillars. → TG pp. 147–150

At home

Count out loud from 1 to 10, leaving some gaps for your child to say the missing number.

21

From garden to plate

a Name the fruits.

b Count the pieces of fruit. Say the total.

At home

Make a fruit salad with your child. Encourage them to talk to you about the flavours and textures of their favourite fruits.

In this session, children will also: find out where fruit grows in their area, make a real fruit salad to eat, play a 'fruit salad' game. → TG pp. 147–150

From garden to plate

a Look. How many children are playing?

b Find the children who look sad.

In this session, children will also: take turns in a game; and review: writing their name, talking about themselves, putting numbers 0–12 in order. → TG pp. 147–150

At home

Talk to your child about the importance of taking turns and being kind to each other.

23

Fun with friends

In this topic, learners are encouraged to:

- discuss other children's feelings
- match things that are similar, but different
- count objects to 20
- identify shapes
- find rhyming words.

Teachers will also help learners to:

- create some artwork about friendship
- explore the outdoor world
- understand the qualities of friendship
- understand how they use the 5 senses
- think about capacity and measurements.

Making friends

a Find Rani's new friend.

b Talk about how Rani feels.

c Count the boys. Count the girls.

d Say the total number of balls.

At home

Practise kicking a ball by taking turns with your child, demonstrating the need for patience and playing fairly.

In this session, children will also: talk about making friends, decide what happens next in a story, practise football skills. → TG pp. 154–157

25

Making friends

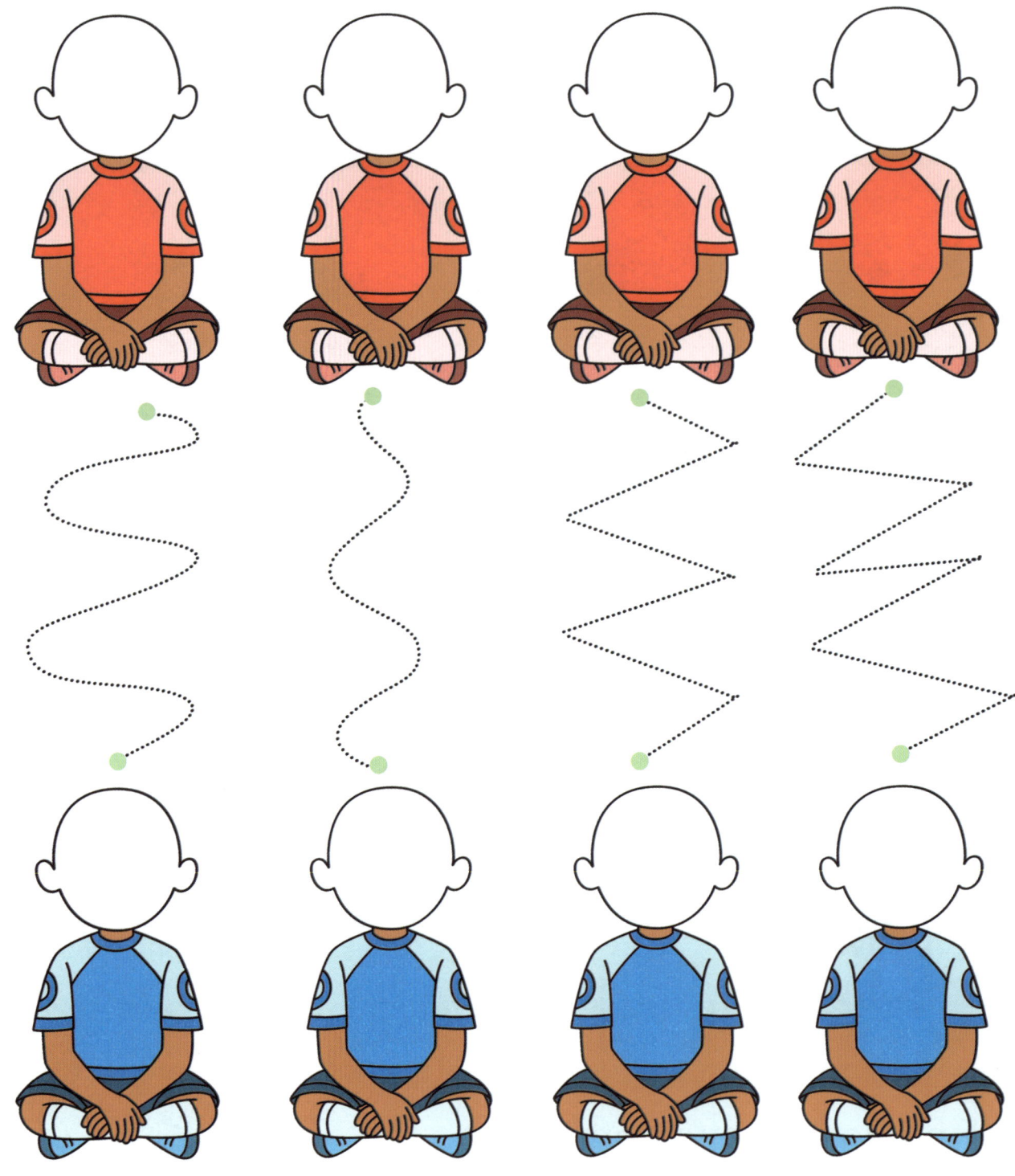

a Draw sad faces on the red team.

b Draw happy faces on the blue team.

c Trace the lines to find their friends.

At home

Play a game of 'hide and seek' together. Talk to your child about how they feel when they are hiding/when they are found.

In this session, children will also: talk about feeling lonely and being friendly, group 8 objects, practise using tweezers to put small objects in lines. → TG pp. 154–157

Making friends

Explore

a Count the animals and say the total.

b Name the animals.

c Match the same type of animal.

At home
Talk with your child about 1 of their friends. What do they have in common? What are the differences between them? What do they like about their friend?

In this session, children will also: talk about their friends, look for similarities and differences, compare handprint pairs, play ball games in pairs. → TG pp. 154–157

Making friends

a Write the number of children.

b Tick (✓) the child who looks happiest.

c Find the children who look worried.

In this session, children will also: try a balancing challenge, set small steps to achieving a goal, paint a picture of themselves achieving a goal. → TG pp. 154–157

At home

Talk to your child about how they can help others when they are worried or sad.

Making friends

Connect

a Look. What are the children doing?

b Count the red beads.

c Find the child who is being a good friend.

In this session, children will also: share stories about friendship, help each other make friendship bracelets, think of ways to help when someone is worried. → TG pp. 154–157

At home

Talk to your child about how to be a good friend and what sort of things a good friend might do.

We are friends

a Say the Friendship rhyme.

b Count the children.

c Look. Which games do you enjoy?

d Find a circle and a rectangle.

In these sessions, children will also: play games with friends outside, make models of playground toys, find rhyming pairs , write CVC words, make some shapes. → TG pp. 158–161

At home

Ask your child to choose a favourite nursery rhyme. Recite it together and act it out. Read other nursery rhymes to them.

31

Explore

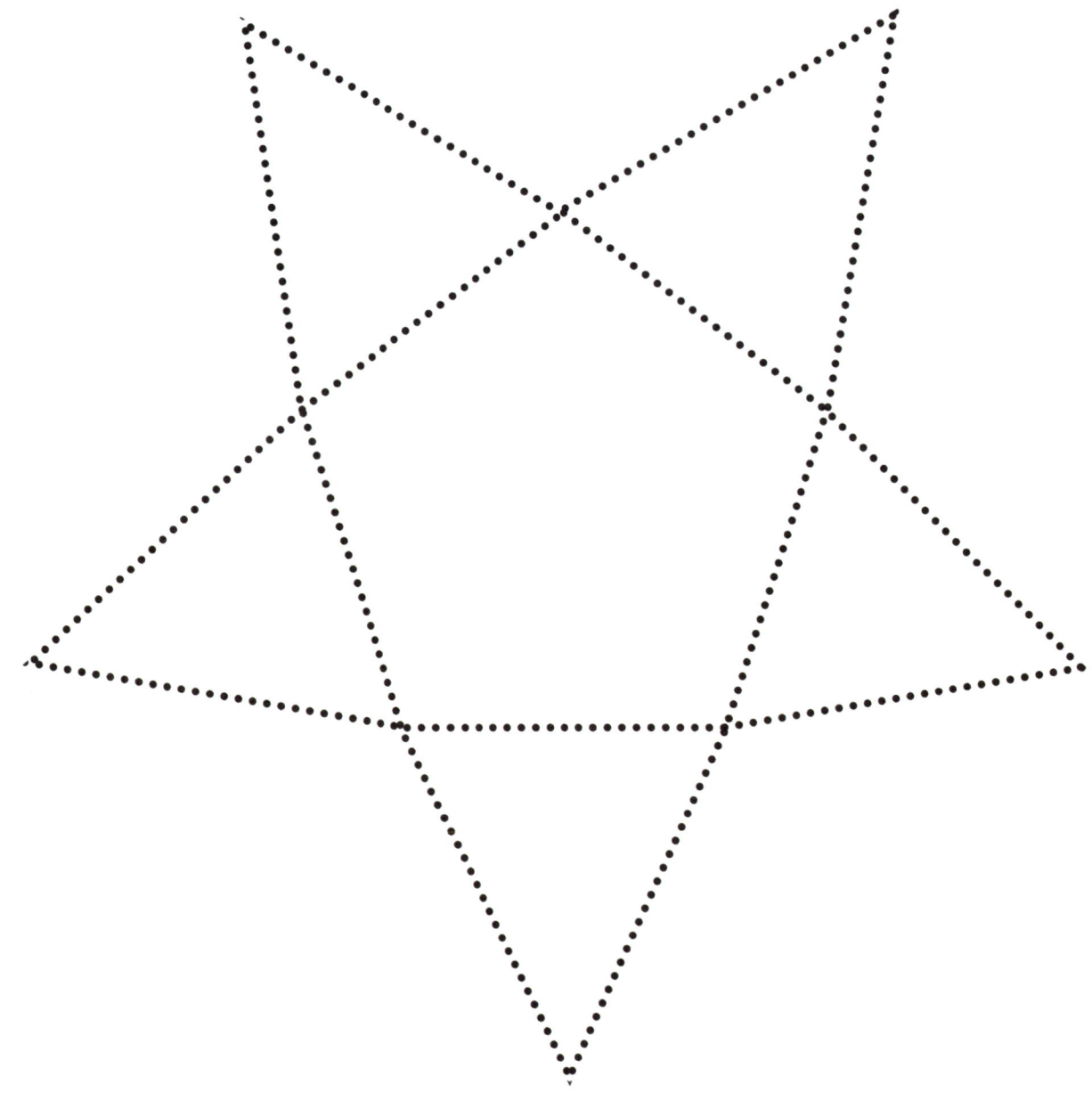

a Count the points on the star.

b Colour the triangles ✺ and the rest of the star ✸.

In this session, children will also: listen to sounds outside, make shape puzzles, play a listening game. → TG pp. 158–161

At home

Look around the house with your child. Can they find shapes such as circles, squares, and triangles?

We are friends

a Find things that make a sound.

b Look. What do you think makes the loudest sound?

In this session, children will also: sing and say rhymes using loud and quiet voices, talk about sounds and their feelings, listen and move around to music. → TG pp. 158–161

At home

With your child, sing a song or say a rhyme very quietly. Then repeat it loudly. Can your child hear the difference?

33

We are friends

1

3

4

7

a Take turns. Count the sets.

b Trace and say the numbers.

c Match each picture with its number.

In this session, children will also: play a counting game, talk about sharing and caring with friends, perform favourite nursery rhymes. → TG pp. 158–161

At home

Talk to your child about games they have played. Ask them why it is important to take turns.

Being a good friend

The friendship bench

1

2

3

4

a Say how Fiona feels in each picture.

b Retell the story.

In this session, children will also: play a counting game, decorate a friendship bench or chair. → TG pp. 161–164

At home

Play a rhyming game by taking turns with your child to find rhymes for simple words like 'cat', 'hen', 'bed', 'jar', etc.

35

Being a good friend

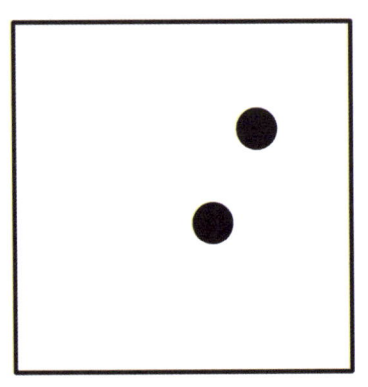 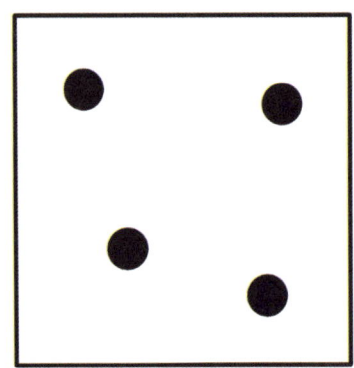 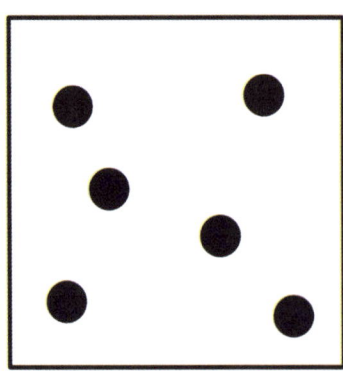

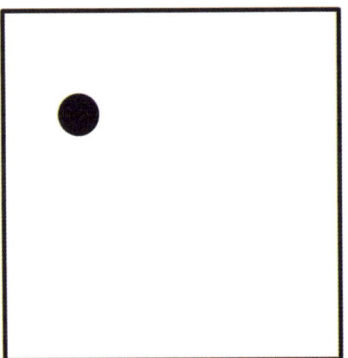 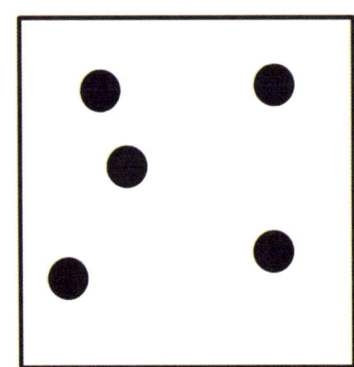 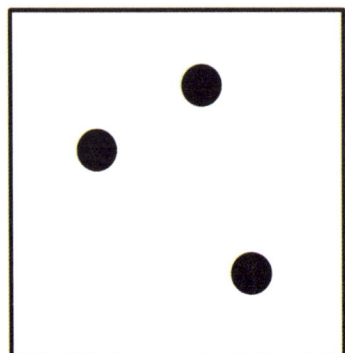

a Colour the square with 3 dots.

b Colour the square with 5 dots.

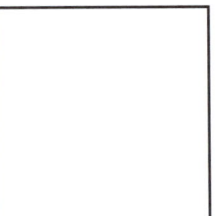  

c Draw dots on these dice faces to show numbers 1 to 6.

At home

Practise throwing a dice with your child and instantly identifying the numbers. Encourage your child to say the number without counting the dots.

In this session, children will also: share stories about friendship, learn new vocabulary, practise using their fingers to represent numbers. → TG pp. 161–164

fun

hugs

help

a Listen to your teacher and colour the friendship bottles.

b Trace and say the words.

At home

With your child, look for bottles in the kitchen cupboard. Can your child tell you which bottles are the fullest?

In this session, children will also: make modelling dough using a recipe, create a friendship 'recipe', compare the capacity of different bottles or containers. → TG pp. 161–164

Being a good friend

bug •

fox •

cat •

hat •

box •

rug •

a Match the rhyming pairs.

b Count the pairs.

In this session, children will also: play a rhyming pairs game, create pictures or models of their friends, practise throwing and counting beanbags. → TG pp. 161–164

At home

Play a game to find rhyming pairs in everyday life. Say a word and ask your child to find a rhyming one. Then swap.

Being a good friend

I am proud of

a Look. What are the children proud of?

b Draw what you are proud of.

In this session, children will also: make stars out of pentagons and triangles, practise ball skills, make jigsaw puzzles. → TG pp. 161–164

At home

Talk with your child about things they are proud of since starting school.

Exploring with friends

a Sing You've got a friend in nature.

b Look. Who is using their nose?

c Count the children who are sharing.

d Find 1 thing that rhymes with 'bat'.

At home

Go into your garden or to the park with your child. Help them write or draw some of the things they see, touch, hear, or smell.

In these sessions, children will also: count to 20 on a number track, create a forest role-play area, revise the seasons, go for a class nature walk, practise sharing. → TG pp. 165–167

Explore

①

②

③

④

a Count the petals and write the number on each flower.

b Match each bee with a flower.

In this session, children will also: make pictures with found natural objects, act out exploring an imaginary forest, play a listening and counting game. → TG pp. 165–167

At home

Do some counting activities with your child outdoors, for example, counting the petals on flowers or the number of steps it takes to cross the grass.

Exploring with friends

a Talk about what snow looks like.

b Say what you think snow feels like.

c Circle which senses the child is using.

In this session, children will also: share stories about playing in the snow, watch ice melting, make frozen pictures. → TG pp. 165–167

At home

Talk with your child about the seasons of the year and the changes in weather. Discuss which outdoor activities you can do at different times of the year.

43

Exploring with friends

a Say what the friends are doing.

b Tick (✓) what you like doing with your friends.

44 In this session, children will also review: names and properties of shapes, hearing and identifying rhyming CVC words, using senses to describe nature. → TG pp. 165–167

At home

Talk with your child about friendships and the qualities a good friend has.

The wonderful world

In this topic, learners are encouraged to:

- explore patterns in nature
- count to 20 and beyond
- contrast night and day
- talk about their daily routines
- find sources of light
- learn about nocturnal animals.

Teachers will also help learners to:

- create pieces of art inspired by nature
- discuss their fears, such as the dark
- develop role-play and storytelling skills
- recognize numbers without counting
- learn about how shadows are made.

Patterns

a Say the We can see a pattern rhyme.

b Describe the patterns.

c Count the children's jackets.

d Look. Who is wearing stripes?

In these sessions, children will also: practise subitizing dot patterns, make patterns with spots and squares on a grid, look at patterns in famous paintings. → TG pp. 168–171

At home

Take your child for a walk and help them identify patterns in nature: leaves on a tree, flower petals, dots on a ladybird, stripes on a caterpillar, etc.

Patterns

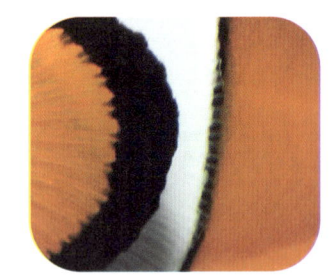

a Name each animal.

b Match each animal with its pattern.

At home

Share some fiction and non-fiction animal books with your child, noticing the patterns on the animals that are featured in them.

In this session, children will also: find out about animal patterns, make their own stripy patterns, play a game to develop their proprioception. → TG pp. 168–171

Patterns

a Count the different colours.

b Finish the pattern.

In this session, children will also: look for examples of patterns in nature, explore and decorate spiral shapes, copy sequences of sounds and movements. → TG pp. 168–171

At home

With your child, look for patterns around you and try to copy them. You could look at leaves, petals, and stones for ideas.

leaf cone

Connect

flower

a Trace the words. Find the objects in the picture.

b Colour the picture.

Make patterns using any natural items you can find with your child. Or you could use buttons, beads, pasta shapes, or coloured crayons if you prefer.

In this session, children will also: work as a group to create transient art, make zig-zag patterns, count and copy repeating patterns. → TG pp. 168–171

Light and colour

a Count the things that make bubbles.

b Name 2 different things that float.

c Find the smallest bubbles.

d Look. Who has the biggest bubble?

At home

Cut the bottom off a clean, disposable plastic bottle. Dip it in a soap and water solution. Ask your child to blow through the top and watch a bubble form!

In these sessions, children will also: blow bubbles, make bubble paintings, write simple phrases, investigate floating and sinking, play balloon games. → TG pp. 172–174

Explore

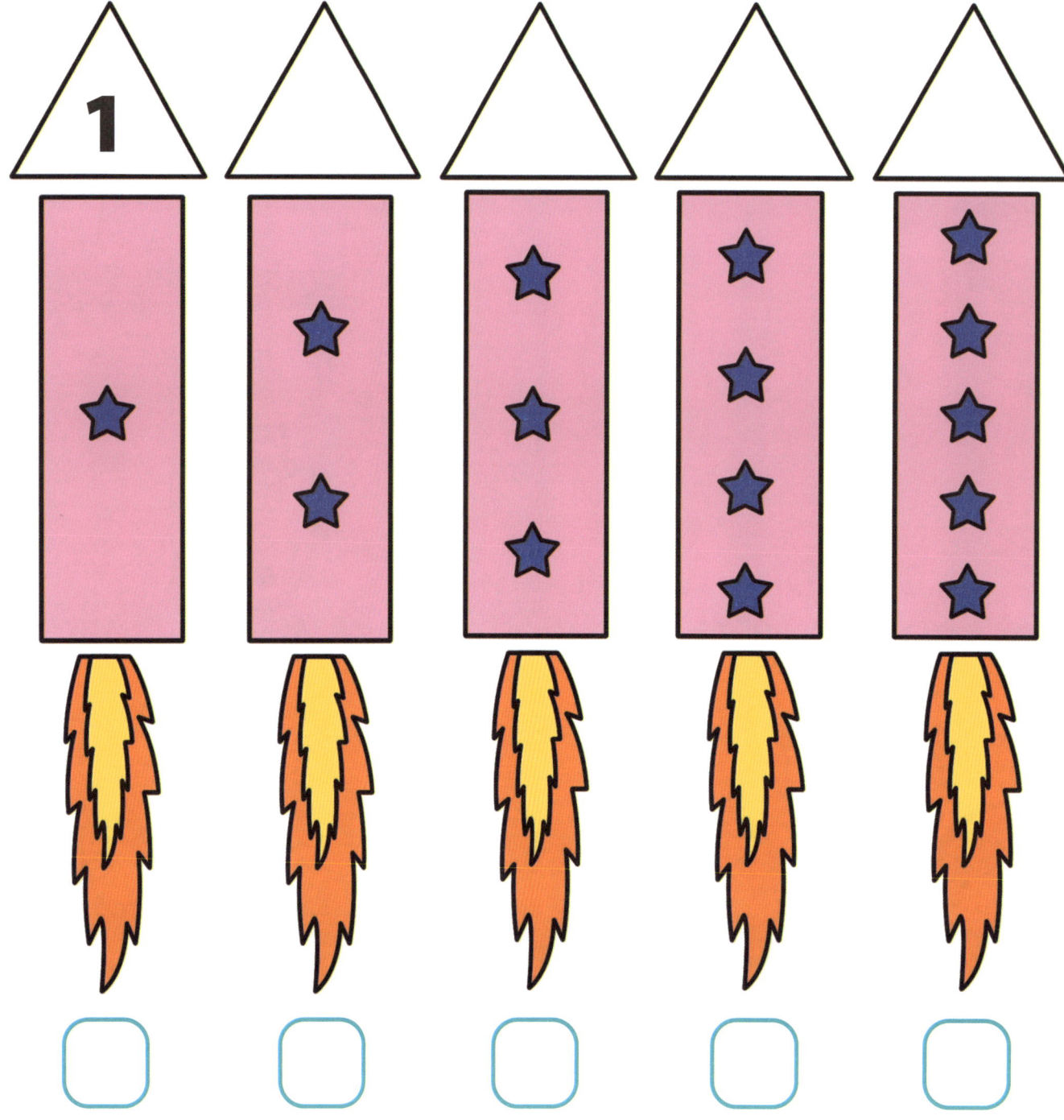

a Look. How many rockets are there?

b Count the stars and write the numbers.

c Tick (✓) the rocket with the most stars.

In this session, children will also: talk about firework displays and how they make them feel, pretend to be fireworks, make a firework picture. → TG pp. 172–174

At home
With your child, draw a rainbow. Help them to count and name the 7 colours.

Light and colour

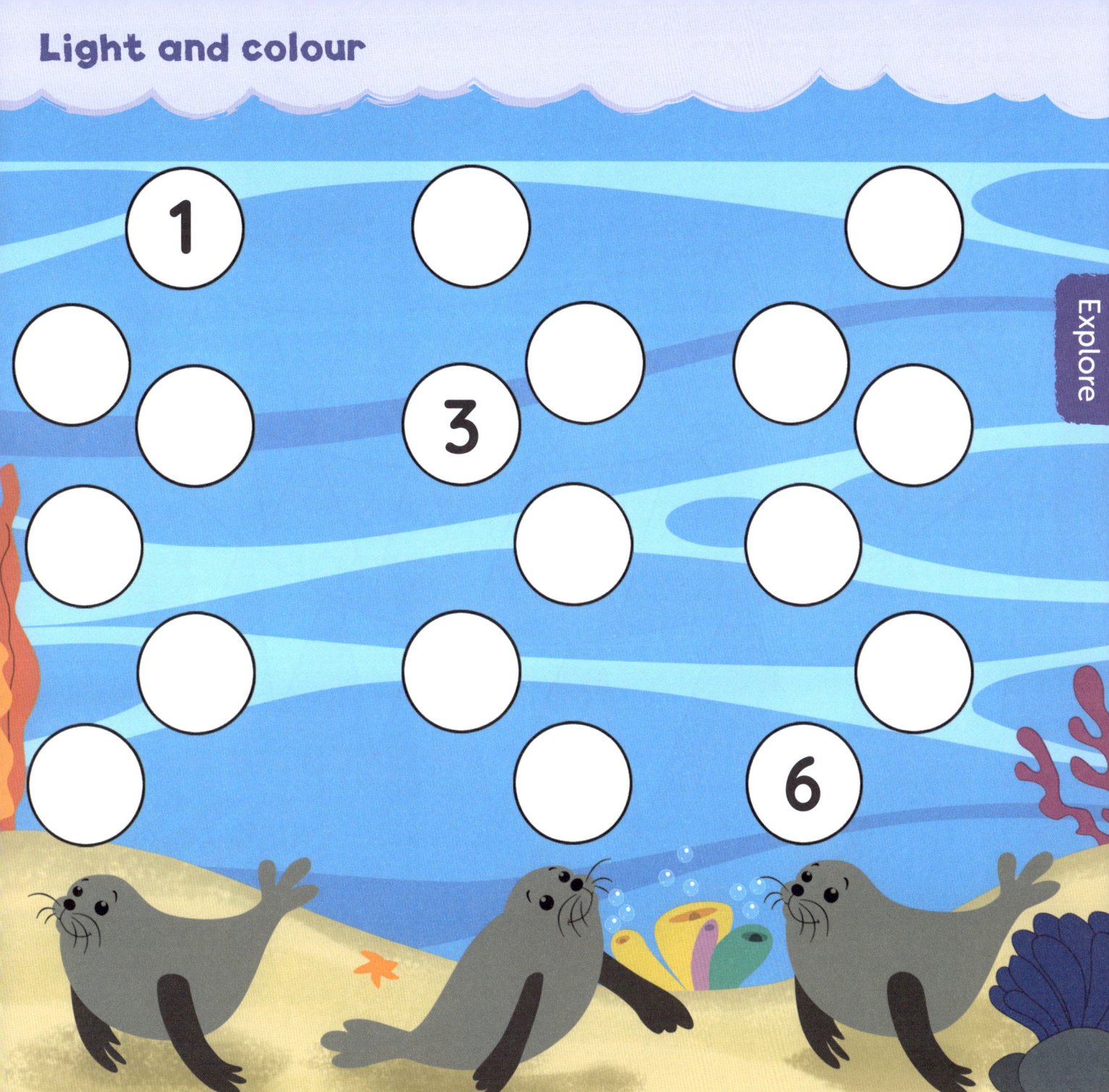

a Count the seals. Count the bubbles.

b Add the missing numbers.

In this session, children will also: make rainbows in different ways, learn the 7 colours of the rainbow, make a rainbow collage. → TG pp. 172–174

At home

Encourage your child to find bubbles and rainbows in your home and local environment. For example, making bubbles when you wash up, or rainbows where the sun shines on oil in a puddle.

53

Connect

a Count the flags.

b Colour the flags in a pattern.

In this session, children will also: find out about special celebrations, make decorations, have their own celebration. → TG pp. 172–174

At home

Talk with your child about how you decorate your home or garden for special occasions.

From night to day

Tarek's night

a Look. Is it night or day in each picture?

b Retell the story.

At home

Talk about what your child does at different times of the day, encouraging them to use words like 'first', 'then', 'after'.

In this session, children will also: look at times on a clock-face, talk about night and day, find out about owls. → TG pp. 175–177

55

From night to day

a Find the building with most windows.

b Colour the things that make light.

In this session, children will also: talk about how they feel about the dark, negotiate obstacles in the dark, make pictures for light to shine through. → TG pp. 175–177

At home

Create some shadow animals with your child by putting your fingers in front of a light source, such as a torch, to throw shadows on the wall.

From night to day

a Tick (✓) the things made by a person.

b Look. Which parts give out light?

In this session, children will also: find out about the sun and the earth, label a 'day/night' picture, observe shadows changing. → TG pp. 175–177

At home

Go around your home with your child, finding all the different items that give out light, such as lamps, ceiling lights, the television, computer screens, etc.

From night to day

Explore

a Colour the frames before school .

b Colour the frames after school .

At home

Talk about different times of the day with your child. Is it dark or light? What activities do you do at different times of the day?

In this session, children will also: count to 12 using a clock-face, count sounds, make up a class story. → TG pp. 175–177

From night to day

1

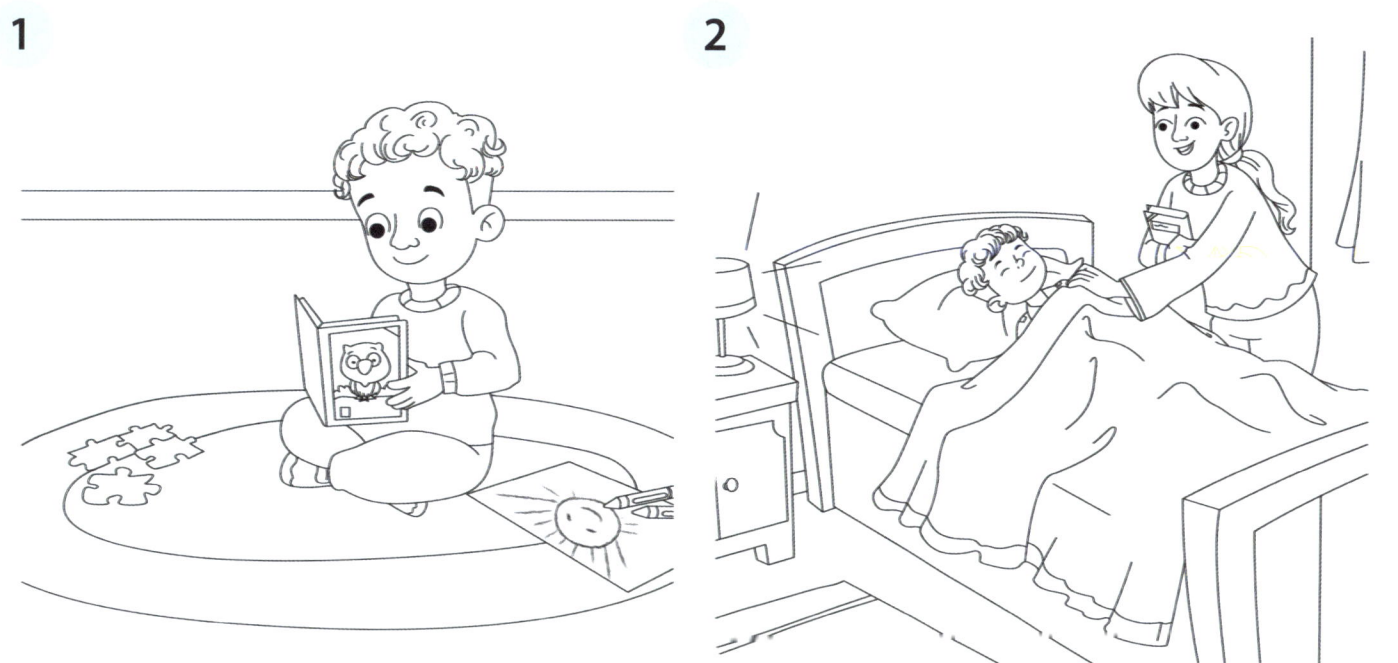

2

3

a Look. What do you do first?

b Say what you do next and then last.

c Colour what you enjoy the most.

At home
Help your child practise the bedtime routine with a teddy or doll. Talk about what comes first, next, and last.

In this session, children will also: talk about the importance of sleep, play and compare being active and being calm, share bedtime stories and songs. → TG pp. 175–177

Fun in the dark

a Sing Day and night.

b Look. Which things give out light?

c Count the children.
Count the adults.

d Find 3 animals.

At home

Talk with your child about animals that come out at night. How many can you think of?

61

In these sessions, children will also: find out about fire, create and play in a pretend campsite, learn about nocturnal animals, use a torch to explore in the dark. → TG pp. 178–180

Fun in the dark

Explore

a Say how many stars without counting.

b Find the boxes with the same number.

Throw a dice with your child. Encourage them to say the numbers they see on the faces, without counting the dots.

In this session, children will also: move like nocturnal animals, put 12 objects into different groups, sing songs and play games around a pretend campfire. → TG pp. 178–180

Fun in the dark

a Match each puppet with its shadow.

b Draw the puppet's shadow.

In this session, children will also: make hand shadows, make shadow puppets, create their own shadow puppet shows. → TG pp. 178–180

At home

Help your child use a table lamp or torch to make some shadows. Experiment with making big and small shadows.

Review

a Name the animals on the board.

b Look. Who is copying the bat?

In this session, children will also: talk about feelings; and review: understanding of day and night, recognizing number patterns, writing CVC words. → TG pp. 178–180

At home

Talk about nocturnal animals with your child. Act out how the animals would move about at night.